sermon notes

FOR KIDS

THESE NOTES BELONG TO:

....

THE NAME OF MY CHURCH IS:

....

A TRUTH STEPS PUBLICATION

sermon notes

FOR KIDS

AGES 6-11

A variety of note-taking
activities designed to
engage kids in worship.

BY JILL CONNELLY

This book is dedicated to
Chloe, Zak, Willow, and Macy.

I have loved worshiping beside you more than
you'll ever know. I pray you always love
to worship as much as you do now.

....

ISBN: 978-0-9859876-0-2

Printed in the United States of America

20 19 18 17 16 15 14 13 12   1 2 3 4

Published by:

Truth Steps Publishing, LLC
Rochester Hills, Michigan
TruthStepsPublishing.com

Design: Darrin Joiner

truthsteps
PUBLISHING

Contents

Note to parents

This book is the product of the last three years of worshiping beside my young children and teaching them how to listen and apply the preaching of God's Word. It is designed for boys and girls ages 6-11.

Each section begins with specific note-taking instructions, tips and extra challenges. The worksheets progress in order of difficulty with the beginning worksheets designed for younger children. A majority of the worksheets can be done independently; however, children learn better when parents are involved in the listening and note-taking process.

It is recommended that the notes be discussed soon after the sermon to ensure understanding and provide an opportunity for your child to ask questions. These conversations will help the preaching of God's Word to infiltrate the rest of your week and give you something to draw from as together your family walks through life's experiences. The benefit? Your child will learn that church is relevant to his life!

I have to admit it is not always easy having my children beside me during the worship service. But it is in those sometimes frustrating moments I am reminded that worship isn't about me. It's completely about the glory and majesty of our Lord Jesus Christ! Psalm 8:1-2.

I was surprised to realize that training my children in corporate worship greatly enhanced my own ability to worship! I suspect this was not a surprise to our Lord! Matthew 19:14, Luke 10:21-22.

Psalm 8:1-2
O LORD, our Lord, how majestic is your name in all the earth! You have set your glory above the heavens. From the lips of children and infants you have ordained praise because of your enemies, to silence the foe and the avenger.

Matthew 19:14
Let the little children come me, and do not hinder them for the kingdom of heaven belongs to such as these.

Luke 10:21-22
I praise you, Father, Lord of heaven and earth, because you have hidden these thin from the wise and learned, and revealed them to little children. Yes, Father, for th was your good pleasure.

For ideas on training your children in corporate wors and to follow my family's journey as we continue to train our children, visit:

 Find us on
Facebook

Facebook.com/SermonNotesFor

 Warning! This note-taking journal has the potential to quickly become a keepsake that you will treasure forever. It has been priceless for me to look back at my children's notes and see how much they have grown in their ability to listen and comprehend even seemingly difficult sermons.

Scripture Scribe

PARENTS: This section is ideal for the younger child who is learning to read and write. Have your child copy from his Bible the main verse(s) of the sermon.

The older child may find it helpful to use Scripture Scribe along with one of the other note-taking sheets, especially if he is having a difficult time listening. Whenever one of my children was struggling to maintain his focus, I would have him take a break from whichever note-taking sheet he was working on and begin using Scripture Scribe to copy the main Bible passage of the sermon.

Remind your child to use his BEST handwriting!

It may be helpful for your child to underline the verse in his Bible before he begins to copy it. This will help keep him from losing his place as he copies.

Offer an incentive to your child to memorize a portion of the text.

Scripture Scribe

KIDS: Copy from your Bible the **KEY VERSE** the preacher is using for his sermon. Give God your best by writing as neatly as you can!

TODAYS DATE: ....

REFERENCE: ....

....

....

....

....

....

....

....

....

....

....

....

....

....

....

....

....

....

....

....

....

....

....

Scripture Scribe

KIDS: Copy from your Bible the **KEY VERSE** the preacher is using for his sermon. Give God your best by writing as neatly as you can!

TODAYS DATE: ....

REFERENCE: ....

....
....
....
....
....
....
....
....
....
....
....
....
....
....
....
....
....
....
....
....
....
....
....

Scripture Scribe

KIDS: Copy from your Bible the **KEY VERSE** the preacher is using for his sermon. Give God your best by writing as neatly as you can!

TODAYS DATE: ....

REFERENCE: ....

....

....

....

....

....

....

....

....

....

....

....

....

....

....

....

....

....

....

Scripture Scribe

KIDS: Copy from your Bible the **KEY VERSE** the preacher is using for his sermon. Give God your best by writing as neatly as you can!

TODAYS DATE: ....

REFERENCE: ....

....

....

....

....

....

....

....

....

....

....

....

....

....

....

....

....

....

....

....

....

....

....

....

....

....

....

Scripture Scribe

KIDS: Copy from your Bible the **KEY VERSE** the preacher is using for his sermon. Give God your best by writing as neatly as you can!

TODAYS DATE: ....

REFERENCE: ....

....

....

....

....

....

....

....

....

....

....

....

....

....

....

....

....

....

....

....

....

Scripture Scribe

KIDS: Copy from your Bible the **KEY VERSE** the preacher is using for his sermon. Give God your best by writing as neatly as you can!

TODAYS DATE: ....

REFERENCE: ....

....

....

....

....

....

....

....

....

....

....

....

....

....

....

....

....

....

....

....

....

Scripture Scribe

KIDS: Copy from your Bible the **KEY VERSE** the preacher is using for his sermon. Give God your best by writing as neatly as you can!

TODAYS DATE: ....

REFERENCE: ....

....

....

....

....

....

....

....

....

....

....

....

....

....

....

....

....

....

....

....

Scripture Scribe

KIDS: Copy from your Bible the **KEY VERSE** the preacher is using for his sermon. Give God your best by writing as neatly as you can!

TODAYS DATE: ....

REFERENCE: ....

....

....

....

....

....

....

....

....

....

....

....

....

....

....

....

....

....

....

....

....

....

....

Scripture Scribe

KIDS: Copy from your Bible the **KEY VERSE** the preacher is using for his sermon. Give God your best by writing as neatly as you can!

TODAYS DATE: ....

REFERENCE: ....

....

....

....

....

....

....

....

....

....

....

....

....

....

....

....

....

....

....

....

....

Scripture Scribe

KIDS: Copy from your Bible the **KEY VERSE** the preacher is using for his sermon. Give God your best by writing as neatly as you can!

TODAYS DATE: ....

REFERENCE: ....

....

....

....

....

....

....

....

....

....

....

....

....

....

....

....

....

....

....

....

....

....

Scripture Scribe

KIDS: Copy from your Bible the **KEY VERSE** the preacher is using for his sermon. Give God your best by writing as neatly as you can!

TODAYS DATE: ....

REFERENCE: ....

....
....
....
....
....
....
....
....
....
....
....
....
....
....
....
....
....
....
....
....
....
....
....
....
....

Scripture Scribe

KIDS: Copy from your Bible the **KEY VERSE** the preacher is using for his sermon. Give God your best by writing as neatly as you can!

TODAYS DATE: ....

REFERENCE: ....

....

....

....

....

....

....

....

....

....

....

....

....

....

....

....

....

....

....

....

....

....

....

Key Word Alphabet

PARENTS: In Key Word Alphabet your child will listen for key words throughout the sermon. Begin by teaching your child how to identify a key word. Have him refrain from writing insignificant words just for the sake of filling in the lines.

This note sheet can be approached in a couple of different ways depending on the age of your child.

My youngest daughter is six years old. Initially, I would tell her the key words throughout the sermon and write the word for her on scrap paper. She would then copy the word to the corresponding letter of the alphabet. It didn't take long before she was able to identify key words on her own and only needed help with the spelling.

Near the end of the service, help your child come up with a sentence that sums up a main point of the sermon. Try to use 2 or 3 key words from the list. Challenge older children to write their own sentence.

 Tip

A good habit to develop is to talk about the sermon on the drive home or around the afternoon meal table.

 **Challenge**

For even more fun, have your family work together to come up with one super long sentence using as many key words as possible. The better everyone was listening to the sermon, the easier it will be to think of a fun run-on sentence containing a lot of key words.

Key Word Alphabet

KIDS: As you listen to the sermon, write down key words that start with as many letters of the alphabet as you can find. Listen for **KEY WORDS** that mean something to the sermon. **Minor, insignificant words do not count.**

A ....   N ....

B ....   O ....

C ....   P ....

D ....   Q ....

E ....   R ....

F ....   S ....

G ....   T ....

H ....   U ....

I ....   V ....

J ....   W ....

K ....   X ....

L ....   Y ....

M ....   Z ....

Using 2 or 3 of your key words, write a sentence that explains one of the main ideas from the sermon.

....

....

....

....

....

Key Word Alphabet

KIDS: As you listen to the sermon, write down key words that start with as many letters of the alphabet as you can find. Listen for **KEY WORDS** that mean something to the sermon. **Minor, insignificant words do not count.**

A ....

B ....

C ....

D ....

E ....

F ....

G ....

H ....

I ....

J ....

K ....

L ....

M ....

N ....

O ....

P ....

Q ....

R ....

S ....

T ....

U ....

V ....

W ....

X ....

Y ....

Z ....

Using 2 or 3 of your key words, write a sentence that explains one of the main ideas from the sermon.

....

....

....

....

....

Key Word Alphabet

KIDS: As you listen to the sermon, write down key words that start with as many letters of the alphabet as you can find. Listen for **KEY WORDS** that mean something to the sermon. **Minor, insignificant words do not count.**

A ....   N ....

B ....   O ....

C ....   P ....

D ....   Q ....

E ....   R ....

F ....   S ....

G ....   T ....

H ....   U ....

I ....   V ....

J ....   W ....

K ....   X ....

L ....   Y ....

M ....   Z ....

Using 2 or 3 of your key words, write a sentence that explains one of the main ideas from the sermon.

....

....

....

....

....

Key Word Alphabet

KIDS: As you listen to the sermon, write down key words that start with as many letters of the alphabet as you can find. Listen for **KEY WORDS** that mean something to the sermon. **Minor, insignificant words do not count.**

A-Z

A ....

B ....

C ....

D ....

E ....

F ....

G ....

H ....

I ....

J ....

K ....

L ....

M ....

N ....

O ....

P ....

Q ....

R ....

S ....

T ....

U ....

V ....

W ....

X ....

Y ....

Z ....

Using 2 or 3 of your key words, write a sentence that explains one of the main ideas from the sermon.

....

....

....

....

....

Key Word Alphabet

A-Z

KIDS: As you listen to the sermon, write down key words that start with as many letters of the alphabet as you can find. Listen for **KEY WORDS** that mean something to the sermon. **Minor, insignificant words do not count.**

A ....

B ....

C ....

D ....

E ....

F ....

G ....

H ....

I ....

J ....

K ....

L ....

M ....

N ....

O ....

P ....

Q ....

R ....

S ....

T ....

U ....

V ....

W ....

X ....

Y ....

Z ....

Using 2 or 3 of your key words, write a sentence that explains one of the main ideas from the sermon.

....

....

....

....

....

Key Word Alphabet

KIDS: As you listen to the sermon, write down key words that start with as many letters of the alphabet as you can find. Listen for **KEY WORDS** that mean something to the sermon. Minor, insignificant words do not count.

A	N
B	O
C	P
D	Q
E	R
F	S
G	T
H	U
I	V
J	W
K	X
L	Y
M	Z

Using 2 or 3 of your key words, write a sentence that explains one of the main ideas from the sermon.

Key Word Alphabet

A-Z

KIDS: As you listen to the sermon, write down key words that start with as many letters of the alphabet as you can find. Listen for **KEY WORDS** that mean something to the sermon. **Minor, insignificant words do not count.**

A ....

B ....

C ....

D ....

E ....

F ....

G ....

H ....

I ....

J ....

K ....

L ....

M ....

N ....

O ....

P ....

Q ....

R ....

S ....

T ....

U ....

V ....

W ....

X ....

Y ....

Z ....

Using 2 or 3 of your key words, write a sentence that explains one of the main ideas from the sermon.

....

....

....

....

....

Key Word Alphabet

KIDS: As you listen to the sermon, write down key words that start with as many letters of the alphabet as you can find. Listen for **KEY WORDS** that mean something to the sermon. **Minor, insignificant words do not count.**

A ....   N ....

B ....   O ....

C ....   P ....

D ....   Q ....

E ....   R ....

F ....   S ....

G ....   T ....

H ....   U ....

I ....   V ....

J ....   W ....

K ....   X ....

L ....   Y ....

M ....   Z ....

Using 2 or 3 of your key words, write a sentence that explains one of the main ideas from the sermon.

....

....

....

....

....

Key Word Alphabet

KIDS: As you listen to the sermon, write down key words that start with as many letters of the alphabet as you can find. Listen for **KEY WORDS** that mean something to the sermon. **Minor, insignificant words do not count.**

A ....

B ....

C ....

D ....

E ....

F ....

G ....

H ....

I ....

J ....

K ....

L ....

M ....

N ....

O ....

P ....

Q ....

R ....

S ....

T ....

U ....

V ....

W ....

X ....

Y ....

Z ....

Using 2 or 3 of your key words, write a sentence that explains one of the main ideas from the sermon.

....

....

....

....

....

Key Word Alphabet

KIDS: As you listen to the sermon, write down key words that start with as many letters of the alphabet as you can find. Listen for **KEY WORDS** that mean something to the sermon. **Minor, insignificant words do not count.**

A ....

B ....

C ....

D ....

E ....

F ....

G ....

H ....

I ....

J ....

K ....

L ....

M ....

N ....

O ....

P ....

Q ....

R ....

S ....

T ....

U ....

V ....

W ....

X ....

Y ....

Z ....

Using 2 or 3 of your key words, write a sentence that explains one of the main ideas from the sermon.

....

....

....

....

....

Key Word Alphabet

KIDS: As you listen to the sermon, write down key words that start with as many letters of the alphabet as you can find. Listen for **KEY WORDS** that mean something to the sermon. **Minor, insignificant words do not count.**

A ....   N ....

B ....   O ....

C ....   P ....

D ....   Q ....

E ....   R ....

F ....   S ....

G ....   T ....

H ....   U ....

I ....   V ....

J ....   W ....

K ....   X ....

L ....   Y ....

M ....   Z ....

Using 2 or 3 of your key words, write a sentence that explains one of the main ideas from the sermon.

....

....

....

....

....

Key Word Alphabet

A-Z

KIDS: As you listen to the sermon, write down key words that start with as many letters of the alphabet as you can find. Listen for **KEY WORDS** that mean something to the sermon. **Minor, insignificant words do not count.**

A ....

B ....

C ....

D ....

E ....

F ....

G ....

H ....

I ....

J ....

K ....

L ....

M ....

N ....

O ....

P ....

Q ....

R ....

S ....

T ....

U ....

V ....

W ....

X ....

Y ....

Z ....

Using 2 or 3 of your key words, write a sentence that explains one of the main ideas from the sermon.

....

....

....

....

Key Word Search

PARENTS: Key Word Search requires a small amount of advance preparation. You will need to fill in some key words for your child to listen for during the sermon.

Before the service, ask the preacher for a few key words from his sermon. You also may be able to come up with some possible key words on your own if you know what the title, Scripture text, and/or main points of the sermon will be.

During the sermon, have your child listen for these words and place a tally mark beside each one as he hears it.

Help your child write down any unfamiliar words or concepts he hears throughout the sermon. Be sure to discuss these soon afterward.

In addition to listening for key words, your child will list all Scripture references read or mentioned throughout the sermon.

 Tip

Ask your pastor for a convenient way to obtain key words. Most pastors will be happy to accommodate you. For instance, my pastor asked that I send him a reminder e-mail on Thursday evening. On Friday morning he replies with a list of key words for Sunday's sermon.

 Challenge

Show your child how to look up unfamiliar words in a Bible dictionary.

Key Word Search

KIDS: Before the service, ask your parents or the preacher for suggested key words to listen for. Place a tally mark next to each word as you hear it.

KEY WORDS: **TALLY MARKS:**

....

....

....

....

....

....

....

....

Words I heard that I don't understand:

List all Scripture references mentioned:

....

....

....

....

Key Word Search

KIDS: Before the service, ask your parents or the preacher for suggested key words to listen for. Place a tally mark next to each word as you hear it.

KEY WORDS:

TALLY MARKS:

....

....

....

....

....

....

....

....

....

....

....

....

....

....

....

....

Words I heard that I don't understand:

List all Scripture references mentioned:

....

....

....

....

....

....

....

....

Key Word Search

KIDS: Before the service, ask your parents or the preacher for suggested key words to listen for. Place a tally mark next to each word as you hear it.

KEY WORDS:

TALLY MARKS:

....

....

....

....

....

....

....

....

Words I heard that I don't understand:

List all Scripture references mentioned:

....

....

....

....

Key Word Search

KIDS: Before the service, ask your parents or the preacher for suggested key words to listen for. Place a tally mark next to each word as you hear it.

KEY WORDS: **TALLY MARKS:**

....

....

....

....

....

....

....

....

Words I heard that I don't understand:

List all Scripture references mentioned:

....

....

....

....

Key Word Search

KIDS: Before the service, ask your parents or the preacher for suggested key words to listen for. Place a tally mark next to each word as you hear it.

KEY WORDS:

TALLY MARKS:

....

....

....

....

....

....

....

....

....

....

....

....

....

....

Words I heard that I don't understand:

List all Scripture references mentioned:

....

....

....

....

....

....

....

....

Key Word Search

KIDS: Before the service, ask your parents or the preacher for suggested key words to listen for. Place a tally mark next to each word as you hear it.

KEY WORDS:

TALLY MARKS:

....

....

....

....

....

....

....

....

....

....

....

....

....

....

Words I heard that I don't understand:

List all Scripture references mentioned:

....

....

....

....

....

....

....

....

Key Word Search

KIDS: Before the service, ask your parents or the preacher for suggested key words to listen for. Place a tally mark next to each word as you hear it.

KEY WORDS: **TALLY MARKS:**

....

....

....

....

....

....

....

....

Words I heard that I don't understand:

List all Scripture references mentioned:

....

....

....

....

Key Word Search

KIDS: Before the service, ask your parents or the preacher for suggested key words to listen for. Place a tally mark next to each word as you hear it.

KEY WORDS:

TALLY MARKS:

....

....

....

....

....

....

....

....

Words I heard that I don't understand:

List all Scripture references mentioned:

....

....

....

....

Key Word Search

KIDS: Before the service, ask your parents or the preacher for suggested key words to listen for. Place a tally mark next to each word as you hear it.

KEY WORDS:

TALLY MARKS:

....

....

....

....

....

....

....

Words I heard that I don't understand:

List all Scripture references mentioned:

Key Word Search

KIDS: Before the service, ask your parents or the preacher for suggested key words to listen for. Place a tally mark next to each word as you hear it.

KEY WORDS:

TALLY MARKS:

....

....

....

....

....

....

....

....

....

....

....

....

....

....

....

....

Words I heard that I don't understand:

List all Scripture references mentioned:

....

....

....

....

....

....

....

....

Key Word Search

KIDS: Before the service, ask your parents or the preacher for suggested key words to listen for. Place a tally mark next to each word as you hear it.

KEY WORDS:

TALLY MARKS:

....

....

....

....

....

....

....

Words I heard that I don't understand:

List all Scripture references mentioned:

Key Word Search

KIDS: Before the service, ask your parents or the preacher for suggested key words to listen for. Place a tally mark next to each word as you hear it.

KEY WORDS: **TALLY MARKS:**

....

....

....

....

....

....

....

....

Words I heard that I don't understand:

List all Scripture references mentioned:

....

....

....

....

Key Word Hangman

PARENTS: Key Word Hangman requires your help and is best used along with one of the other note-taking sheets. I often use this sheet a little later in a sermon, especially if my child is having difficulty listening or has a lull in his note-taking.

Choose a mystery key word or phrase from the sermon. Use the empty space provided to mark out your lines for each letter of your word or phrase.

For the sake of being quiet, have your child circle the letter of his choice rather than tell you. Then you make a slash mark across the circled letter and fill in the corresponding blank of the mystery word. If it is a wrong guess, draw part of the hangman.

Once the mystery word is figured out, have him use the space provided to write a sentence about the significance or meaning of the word as it relates to the sermon.

⚠ Tips

Key Word Hangman is fun to play near the end of a sermon.

Draw a shape other than a man. A simple box house or 5-pointed star works great.

◎ Challenge

Reverse your roles. Have your child come up with a mystery word or phrase for you to figure out.

Key Word Hangman

KIDS: Ask Dad or Mom to choose a mystery key word or phrase from the sermon. After you figure out the word, write a sentence describing how the word or phrase relates to the sermon.

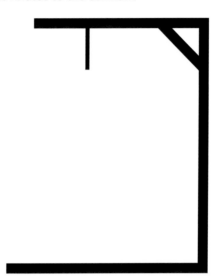

Mystery key word/phrase:

A   B   C   D   E   F   G   H   I   J   K   L   M
N   O   P   Q   R   S   T   U   V   W   X   Y   Z

Sentence about key word:

Key Word Hangman

KIDS: Ask Dad or Mom to choose a mystery key word or phrase from the sermon. After you figure out the word, write a sentence describing how the word or phrase relates to the sermon.

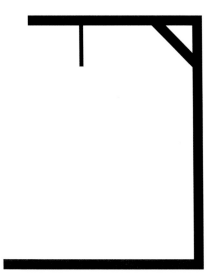

Mystery key word/phrase:

A B C D E F G H I J K L M
N O P Q R S T U V W X Y Z

Sentence about key word:

Key Word Hangman

KIDS: Ask Dad or Mom to choose a mystery key word or phrase from the sermon. After you figure out the word, write a sentence describing how the word or phrase relates to the sermon.

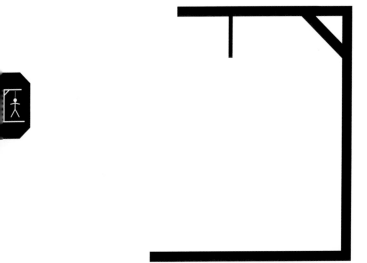

Mystery key word/phrase:

A B C D E F G H I J K L M
N O P Q R S T U V W X Y Z

Sentence about key word:

Key Word Hangman

KIDS: Ask Dad or Mom to choose a mystery key word or phrase from the sermon. After you figure out the word, write a sentence describing how the word or phrase relates to the sermon.

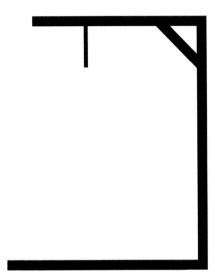

Mystery key word/phrase:

A B C D E F G H I J K L M
N O P Q R S T U V W X Y Z

Sentence about key word:

....
....
....
....

Key Word Hangman

KIDS: Ask Dad or Mom to choose a mystery key word or phrase from the sermon. After you figure out the word, write a sentence describing how the word or phrase relates to the sermon.

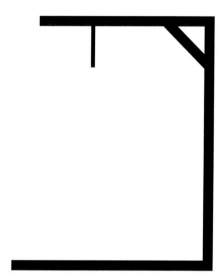

Mystery key word/phrase:

A B C D E F G H I J K L M
N O P Q R S T U V W X Y Z

Sentence about key word:

Key Word Hangman

KIDS: Ask Dad or Mom to choose a mystery key word or phrase from the sermon. After you figure out the word, write a sentence describing how the word or phrase relates to the sermon.

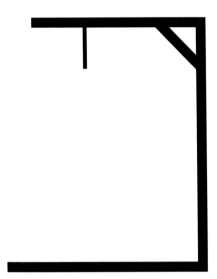

Mystery key word/phrase:

A   B   C   D   E   F   G   H   I   J   K   L   M
N   O   P   Q   R   S   T   U   V   W   X   Y   Z

Sentence about key word:

Key Word Hangman

KIDS: Ask Dad or Mom to choose a mystery key word or phrase from the sermon. After you figure out the word, write a sentence describing how the word or phrase relates to the sermon.

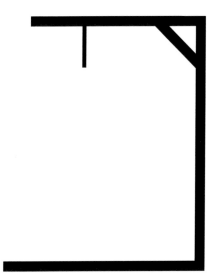

Mystery key word/phrase:

A   B   C   D   E   F   G   H   I   J   K   L   M

N   O   P   Q   R   S   T   U   V   W   X   Y   Z

Sentence about key word:

Key Word Hangman

KIDS: Ask Dad or Mom to choose a mystery key word or phrase from the sermon. After you figure out the word, write a sentence describing how the word or phrase relates to the sermon.

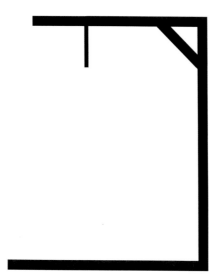

Mystery key word/phrase:

A   B   C   D   E   F   G   H   I   J   K   L   M
N   O   P   Q   R   S   T   U   V   W   X   Y   Z

Sentence about key word:

Key Word Hangman

KIDS: Ask Dad or Mom to choose a mystery key word or phrase from the sermon. After you figure out the word, write a sentence describing how the word or phrase relates to the sermon.

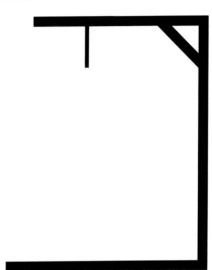

Mystery key word/phrase:

A   B   C   D   E   F   G   H   I   J   K   L   M

N   O   P   Q   R   S   T   U   V   W   X   Y   Z

Sentence about key word:

Key Word Hangman

KIDS: Ask Dad or Mom to choose a mystery key word or phrase from the sermon. After you figure out the word, write a sentence describing how the word or phrase relates to the sermon.

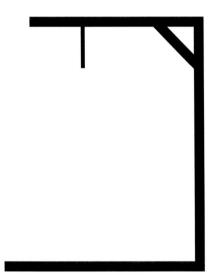

Mystery key word/phrase:

A B C D E F G H I J K L M
N O P Q R S T U V W X Y Z

Sentence about key word:

Key Word Hangman

KIDS: Ask Dad or Mom to choose a mystery key word or phrase from the sermon. After you figure out the word, write a sentence describing how the word or phrase relates to the sermon.

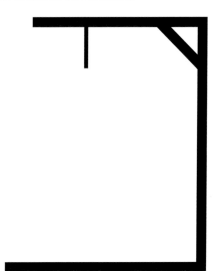

Mystery key word/phrase:

A B C D E F G H I J K L M

N O P Q R S T U V W X Y Z

Sentence about key word:

Key Word Hangman

KIDS: Ask Dad or Mom to choose a mystery key word or phrase from the sermon. After you figure out the word, write a sentence describing how the word or phrase relates to the sermon.

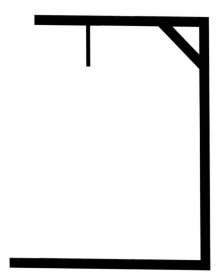

Mystery key word/phrase:

A B C D E F G H I J K L M
N O P Q R S T U V W X Y Z

Sentence about key word:

Sermon Illustrator

PARENTS: Even as an adult, one of my favorite methods of sermon note-taking is to visualize the sermon by drawing pictures. Some sermons lend themselves to this method more than others.

Have your child use his imagination to draw pictures of a couple of the main points or ideas of the sermon. Be sure to ask your child to tell you about his drawings to check his understanding of the sermon.

 Tip

Complete your own sermon illustration. Your child will enjoy comparing your drawing with his own.

 Challenge

Near the end of the sermon, have your child use one of the boxes to illustrate how he can apply the message to his life.

Sermon Illustrator

KIDS: Illustrate the main points of the sermon. Be creative in drawing what the sermon is about.

Sermon Illustrator

KIDS: Illustrate the main points of the sermon. Be creative in drawing what the sermon is about.

Sermon Illustrator

KIDS: Illustrate the main points of the sermon. Be creative in drawing what the sermon is about.

Sermon Illustrator

KIDS: Illustrate the main points of the sermon. Be creative in drawing what the sermon is about.

Sermon Illustrator

KIDS: Illustrate the main points of the sermon. Be creative in drawing what the sermon is about.

Sermon Illustrator

KIDS: Illustrate the main points of the sermon. Be creative in drawing what the sermon is about.

Sermon Illustrator

KIDS: Illustrate the main points of the sermon. Be creative in drawing what the sermon is about.

Sermon Illustrator

KIDS: Illustrate the main points of the sermon. Be creative in drawing what the sermon is about.

Sermon Illustrator

KIDS: Illustrate the main points of the sermon. Be creative in drawing what the sermon is about.

Sermon Illustrator

KIDS: Illustrate the main points of the sermon. Be creative in drawing what the sermon is about.

Sermon Illustrator

KIDS: Illustrate the main points of the sermon. Be creative in drawing what the sermon is about.

Sermon Illustrator

KIDS: Illustrate the main points of the sermon. Be creative in drawing what the sermon is about.

Sermon Outline

PARENTS: Sermon Outline is a nice challenge for the older child. It requires that he listen for and identify the preacher's main points of the sermon. Have your child also include supporting Scripture references for each point when possible.

To finish, have your child write a sentence or two summarizing how the sermon will help him grow spiritually or help him during the week with friends, school, teachers, family, etc.

 Tip

Most preachers have between three and five main points

 **Challenge**

Have your child come up with a good title for the sermon.

Sermon Outline

KIDS: Write down several main points or ideas presented by the preacher. Include Scripture references when possible.

1. ....
....
....

2. ....
....
....

3. ....
....
....

4. ....
....
....

5. ....
....
....

How can you apply this to your life during the week?

....
....
....
....

Sermon Outline

KIDS: Write down several main points or ideas presented by the preacher. Include Scripture references when possible.

1. ....
....
....

2. ....
....
....

3. ....
....
....

4. ....
....
....

5. ....
....
....

How can you apply this to your life during the week?

....
....
....
....

Sermon Outline

KIDS: Write down several main points or ideas presented by the preacher. Include Scripture references when possible.

1. ....
....
....

2. ....
....
....

3. ....
....
....

4. ....
....
....

5. ....
....
....

How can you apply this to your life during the week?

....
....
....
....

Sermon Outline

KIDS: Write down several main points or ideas presented by the preacher. Include Scripture references when possible.

1. ....
....
....

2. ....
....
....

3. ....
....
....

4. ....
....
....

5. ....
....
....

How can you apply this to your life during the week?

....
....
....
....

Sermon Outline

KIDS: Write down several main points or ideas presented by the preacher. Include Scripture references when possible.

1. ....
   ....
   ....

2. ....
   ....
   ....

3. ....
   ....
   ....

4. ....
   ....
   ....

5. ....
   ....
   ....

How can you apply this to your life during the week?

....
....
....
....

Sermon Outline

KIDS: Write down several main points or ideas presented by the preacher. Include Scripture references when possible.

1. ....
....
....

2. ....
....
....

3. ....
....
....

4. ....
....
....

5. ....
....
....

How can you apply this to your life during the week?

....
....
....
....

Sermon Outline

KIDS: Write down several main points or ideas presented by the preacher. Include Scripture references when possible.

1. ....
....
....

2. ....
....
....

3. ....
....
....

4. ....
....
....

5. ....
....
....

How can you apply this to your life during the week?

....
....
....
....

Sermon Outline

KIDS: Write down several main points or ideas presented by the preacher. Include Scripture references when possible.

1. ....
....
....

2. ....
....
....

3. ....
....
....

4. ....
....
....

5. ....
....
....

How can you apply this to your life during the week?

....
....
....
....

Sermon Outline

KIDS: Write down several main points or ideas presented by the preacher. Include Scripture references when possible.

1. ....
....
....

2. ....
....
....

3. ....
....
....

4. ....
....
....

5. ....
....
....

How can you apply this to your life during the week?

....
....
....
....

Sermon Outline

KIDS: Write down several main points or ideas presented by the preacher. Include Scripture references when possible.

1. ....
....
....

2. ....
....
....

3. ....
....
....

4. ....
....
....

5. ....
....
....

How can you apply this to your life during the week?

....
....
....
....

Sermon Outline

KIDS: Write down several main points or ideas presented by the preacher. Include Scripture references when possible.

1. ....
....
....

2. ....
....
....

3. ....
....
....

4. ....
....
....

5. ....
....
....

How can you apply this to your life during the week?

....
....
....
....

Sermon Outline

KIDS: Write down several main points or ideas presented by the preacher. Include Scripture references when possible.

1. ....
....
....

2. ....
....
....

3. ....
....
....

4. ....
....
....

5. ....
....
....

How can you apply this to your life during the week?

....
....
....
....

Sermon Notes

PARENTS: In this section, your child can take notes however he would prefer. The lined pages can be used for writing out Scripture verses, key words and phrases, or for writing the main points of an outline.

The unlined pages can be used for more sermon illustrations or hangman. You might even come up with your own ideas on things to listen for or methods for taking notes.

 Tip

If the sermon's Scripture text is made known in advance of Sunday's service, read and discuss it with your child. Being familiar with the passage will increase your child's listening power.

 **Challenge**

Come up with a new method for note-taking. You could even e-mail the author or publisher of this book to share your idea!

Sermon Notes

KIDS: Take notes however you like.

DATE: .... **SCRIPTURE:** ....

Sermon Notes

KIDS: Take notes however you like.

DATE: .... **SCRIPTURE:** ....

Sermon Notes

KIDS: Take notes however you like.

DATE: .... SCRIPTURE: ....

Sermon Notes

KIDS: Take notes however you like.

DATE: .... **SCRIPTURE:** ....

Sermon Notes

KIDS: Take notes however you like.

DATE: .... **SCRIPTURE:** ....

Sermon Notes

KIDS: Take notes however you like.

DATE: .... **SCRIPTURE:** ....

Sermon Notes

KIDS: Take notes however you like.

DATE: ....   **SCRIPTURE:** ....

Sermon Notes

KIDS: Take notes however you like.

DATE:.. **SCRIPTURE:**...

Sermon Notes

KIDS: Take notes however you like.

DATE: .... **SCRIPTURE:** ....

Sermon Notes

KIDS: Take notes however you like.

DATE: .... **SCRIPTURE:** ....

Sermon Notes

KIDS: Take notes however you like.

DATE: .... **SCRIPTURE:** ....

Sermon Notes

KIDS: Take notes however you like.

DATE: .... **SCRIPTURE:** ....

Missionary Moments

PARENTS: When I was growing up, I often found it difficult to listen to guest missionary speakers. Their slides and stories all seemed to look and sound alike. This form helps give children specific things to listen for and helps them better understand the differences between the various missionaries your church may support.

Missionary speakers present a great opportunity for your child to use the Guest Log in the back of this book. Before or after the service, have your child introduce himself to the missionary and ask him to sign his name along with his favorite Scripture reference.

 Tip

At the start of the service or presentation, have your child become familiar with the Missionary Moment questions, since they may not be answered in the order given.

 **Challenge**

Have a family quiz on the way home or around the meal table asking each other trivia questions about the missionary.

Find the missionary's country on a map, globe, or atlas.

Missionary Moments

Missionary name: ....

Country serving in: ....

In what continent is this country located? ....

Is the missionary's spouse present? ☐ YES ☐ NO

Do they have children? ☐ YES ☐ NO How many? ....

Were pictures/video shown? ☐ YES ☐ NO

What is the main ministry? ☐ Church Plant ☐ Medical ☐ Education

☐ Construction ☐ Special Interest Group

☐ Other: ....

What passage of Scripture did he or she share from?

....

List specific prayer requests given:

....

....

....

What interested you most about the missionary?

....

....

....

....

Ask the missionary to sign your **Guest Log** in the back of this book!

Missionary Moments

Missionary name: ....

Country serving in: ....

In what continent is this country located? ....

Is the missionary's spouse present? ☐ YES ☐ NO

Do they have children? ☐ YES ☐ NO   How many? ....

Were pictures/video shown? ☐ YES ☐ NO

What is the main ministry? ☐ Church Plant   ☐ Medical   ☐ Education

☐ Construction   ☐ Special Interest Group

☐ Other: ....

What passage of Scripture did he or she share from?

....

List specific prayer requests given:

....

....

....

What interested you most about the missionary?

....

....

....

....

Ask the missionary to sign your **Guest Log** in the back of this book!

Missionary Moments

Missionary name: ....

Country serving in: ....

In what continent is this country located?..

Is the missionary's spouse present? ☐ YES   ☐ NO

Do they have children? ☐ YES   ☐ NO   How many? ....

Were pictures/video shown? ☐ YES   ☐ NO

What is the main ministry? ☐ Church Plant   ☐ Medical   ☐ Education

☐ Construction   ☐ Special Interest Group

☐ Other: ....

What passage of Scripture did he or she share from?

....

List specific prayer requests given:

....

....

....

What interested you most about the missionary?

....

....

....

....

Ask the missionary to sign your **Guest Log** in the back of this book!

Missionary Moments

Missionary name: ....

Country serving in: ....

In what continent is this country located? ....

Is the missionary's spouse present? ☐ YES ☐ NO

Do they have children? ☐ YES ☐ NO **How many?** ....

Were pictures/video shown? ☐ YES ☐ NO

What is the main ministry? ☐ Church Plant ☐ Medical ☐ Education

☐ Construction ☐ Special Interest Group

☐ Other: ....

What passage of Scripture did he or she share from?

....

List specific prayer requests given:

....

....

....

What interested you most about the missionary?

....

....

....

....

Ask the missionary to sign your **Guest Log** in the back of this book!

Missionary Moments

Missionary name: ....

Country serving in: ....

In what continent is this country located? ....

Is the missionary's spouse present? ☐ YES   ☐ NO

Do they have children? ☐ YES   ☐ NO   How many? ....

Were pictures/video shown? ☐ YES   ☐ NO

What is the main ministry?   ☐ Church Plant   ☐ Medical   ☐ Education

☐ Construction   ☐ Special Interest Group

☐ Other: ....

What passage of Scripture did he or she share from?

....

List specific prayer requests given:

....

....

....

What interested you most about the missionary?

....

....

....

....

Ask the missionary to sign your **Guest Log** in the back of this book!

Missionary Moments

Missionary name: ....

Country serving in: ....

In what continent is this country located? ....

Is the missionary's spouse present? ☐ YES ☐ NO

Do they have children? ☐ YES ☐ NO   How many? ....

Were pictures/video shown? ☐ YES ☐ NO

What is the main ministry? ☐ Church Plant   ☐ Medical   ☐ Education

☐ Construction   ☐ Special Interest Group

☐ Other: ....

What passage of Scripture did he or she share from?

....

List specific prayer requests given:

....

....

....

What interested you most about the missionary?

....

....

....

....

Ask the missionary to sign your **Guest Log** in the back of this book!

Missionary Moments

Missionary name: ....

Country serving in: ....

In what continent is this country located? ....

Is the missionary's spouse present? ☐ YES   ☐ NO

Do they have children? ☐ YES   ☐ NO   How many? ....

Were pictures/video shown? ☐ YES   ☐ NO

What is the main ministry? ☐ Church Plant   ☐ Medical   ☐ Education

☐ Construction   ☐ Special Interest Group

☐ Other: ....

What passage of Scripture did he or she share from?

....

List specific prayer requests given:

....

....

....

What interested you most about the missionary?

....

....

....

....

Ask the missionary to sign your **Guest Log** in the back of this book!

Missionary Moments

Missionary name: ....

Country serving in: ....

In what continent is this country located? ....

Is the missionary's spouse present? ☐ YES ☐ NO

Do they have children? ☐ YES ☐ NO How many? ....

Were pictures/video shown? ☐ YES ☐ NO

What is the main ministry? ☐ Church Plant ☐ Medical ☐ Education

☐ Construction ☐ Special Interest Group

☐ Other: ....

What passage of Scripture did he or she share from?

....

List specific prayer requests given:

....

....

....

What interested you most about the missionary?

....

....

....

....

Ask the missionary to sign your **Guest Log** in the back of this book!

Missionary Moments

Missionary name: ....

Country serving in: ....

In what continent is this country located?...

Is the missionary's spouse present? ☐ YES ☐ NO

Do they have children? ☐ YES ☐ NO How many? ....

Were pictures/video shown? ☐ YES ☐ NO

What is the main ministry? ☐ Church Plant ☐ Medical ☐ Education

☐ Construction ☐ Special Interest Group

☐ Other: ....

What passage of Scripture did he or she share from?

....

List specific prayer requests given:

....

....

....

What interested you most about the missionary?

....

....

....

....

Ask the missionary to sign your **Guest Log** in the back of this book!

Missionary Moments

Missionary name: ....

Country serving in: ....

In what continent is this country located? ....

Is the missionary's spouse present? ☐ YES ☐ NO

Do they have children? ☐ YES ☐ NO How many? ....

Were pictures/video shown? ☐ YES ☐ NO

What is the main ministry? ☐ Church Plant ☐ Medical ☐ Education

☐ Construction ☐ Special Interest Group

☐ Other: ....

What passage of Scripture did he or she share from?

....

List specific prayer requests given:

....

....

....

What interested you most about the missionary?

....

....

....

....

Ask the missionary to sign your **Guest Log** in the back of this book!

Prayer Meeting

PARENTS: If your child sits with you during prayer meeting, these note sheets can encourage your child to listen and participate.

If a devotional or teaching from Scripture is given, have your child write out the main verse in the box provided. If not, have him write one of his own favorite Bible verses.

Space is provided for your child to listen for and write down a few answers to prayer. Have your child write down any of his own recent answers to prayer.

The next section is for your child to write a few of his own prayer requests. Encourage him to come up with at least one request he might like for someone to pray on his behalf. Ask him if he would like to make the request public.

As your child listens to prayer requests given by others, have him list the ones he thinks he might enjoy praying for.

 Tip

God delights in a child's prayer as much as an adult's!

 **Challenge**

Encourage your child to follow through with praying for the requests during the week ahead.

Prayer Meeting

Special Bible Verse:

Praise / Answered Prayers:

....

....

....

....

My personal prayer requests:

....

....

....

....

Requests of others I would like to pray for:

....

....

....

....

Prayer Meeting

Special Bible Verse:

Praise / Answered Prayers:

....

....

....

....

....

My personal prayer requests:

....

....

....

....

Requests of others I would like to pray for:

....

....

....

....

....

Prayer Meeting

Special Bible Verse:

Praise / Answered Prayers:

My personal prayer requests:

Requests of others I would like to pray for:

Prayer Meeting

Special Bible Verse:

Praise / Answered Prayers:

My personal prayer requests:

Requests of others I would like to pray for:

Prayer Meeting

Special Bible Verse:

Praise / Answered Prayers:

My personal prayer requests:

Requests of others I would like to pray for:

Prayer Meeting

Special Bible Verse:

Praise / Answered Prayers:

My personal prayer requests:

Requests of others I would like to pray for:

Prayer Meeting

Special Bible Verse:

Praise / Answered Prayers:

My personal prayer requests:

Requests of others I would like to pray for:

Prayer Meeting

Special Bible Verse:

Praise / Answered Prayers:

....

....

....

....

....

My personal prayer requests:

....

....

....

....

Requests of others I would like to pray for:

....

....

....

....

....

Prayer Meeting

Special Bible Verse:

Praise / Answered Prayers:

My personal prayer requests:

Requests of others I would like to pray for:

Prayer Meeting

Special Bible Verse:

Praise / Answered Prayers:

My personal prayer requests:

Requests of others I would like to pray for:

Prayer Meeting

Special Bible Verse:

Praise / Answered Prayers:

My personal prayer requests:

Requests of others I would like to pray for:

Prayer Meeting

Special Bible Verse:

Praise / Answered Prayers:

My personal prayer requests:

Requests of others I would like to pray for:

Prayer Meeting

Special Bible Verse:

Praise / Answered Prayers:

My personal prayer requests:

Requests of others I would like to pray for:

Prayer Meeting

Special Bible Verse:

Praise / Answered Prayers:

My personal prayer requests:

Requests of others I would like to pray for:

Communion

"This do in remembrance of Me"

PARENTS: This section on communion is not for note-taking purposes. If your child participates in communion, this is a guide for what he could be praying and thinking about while communion is being administered.

If your child does not participate in communion, he can still follow along with this communion guide. It is a great tool for helping him learn and understand the purpose of communion.

I have also included a blank page so you can write your own thought prompts or suggestions to guide your child's mind during this special time of remembrance for what Christ accomplished for us on the cross.

 Tip

Even if your child does not physically participate in communion, he is more than capable of participating mentally.

 **Challenge**

Memorize Psalm 100 together as a family.

Communion

"This do in remembrance of Me"

KIDS: Below are some thoughts and Scripture for you to read and think about during communion.

1) **REMEMBER** – Spend some time reading about Christ's death, burial, resurrection, and last supper. Choose one of the Gospel accounts below.

	DEATH, BURIAL, RESURRECTION	LAST SUPPER
1.	Matthew 27:26 – 28:7	Matthew 26:26-30
2.	Mark 15:21 – 16:7	Mark 14:22-26
3.	Luke 23:26 – 24:8	Luke 22:14-20
4.	John 19:16 – 20:9	1 Corinthians 11:23-32

2) **CONFESSION** – Are there any sins you have not yet told God you are sorry for? Take a couple minutes to ask God to reveal anything in your heart that is not pleasing to Him. Then repent and ask forgiveness.

Search me, O God, and know my heart;
test me and know my anxious thoughts.
Point out anything in me that offends you,
and lead me along the path of everlasting life.
- Psalm 139:23-24 (NLT)

3) **PRAISE** – Spend the last few moments praising and thanking God for who He is. Below are listed a few great praise Psalms.

Psalm 93	Psalm 97
Psalm 94	Psalm 98
Psalm 95	Psalm 99
Psalm 96	Psalm 100

Communion

"This do in remembrance of Me"

Dad or Mom's suggestions for you: ....

....

....

....

....

....

....

....

....

....

....

....

....

....

....

....

....

....

....

....

....

....

Guest Speaker Log

PARENTS: The Guest Speaker Log provides a great opportunity for your child to interact with guest preachers. First, teach your child how to properly introduce himself.

After the service, he can introduce himself to the guest speaker and ask him to sign the Guest Log. Remind your child to ask the speaker to include his favorite Scripture reference.

 Tip

Occasionally practice proper introductions at home to help your child gain confidence in introducing himself to adults.

 **Challenge**

Have your child show his sermon notes to the guest speaker.

Look up the Scripture reference the speaker wrote to see why it might be his favorite verse.

Guest Speaker Log

KIDS: Whenever there is a guest speaker or missionary, ask him to sign his name and favorite Scripture reference.

Guest Speaker	Scripture Reference

Guest Speaker Log

KIDS: Whenever there is a guest speaker or missionary, ask him to sign his name and favorite Scripture reference.

....	....
Guest Speaker	Scripture Reference
....	....
Guest Speaker	Scripture Reference
....	....
Guest Speaker	Scripture Reference
....	....
Guest Speaker	Scripture Reference
....	....
Guest Speaker	Scripture Reference
....	....
Guest Speaker	Scripture Reference
....	....
Guest Speaker	Scripture Reference
....	....
Guest Speaker	Scripture Reference
....	....
Guest Speaker	Scripture Reference
....	....
Guest Speaker	Scripture Reference
....	....
Guest Speaker	Scripture Reference
....	....
Guest Speaker	Scripture Reference
....	....
Guest Speaker	Scripture Reference
....	....
Guest Speaker	Scripture Reference
....	....
Guest Speaker	Scripture Reference
....	....
Guest Speaker	Scripture Reference

Guest Speaker Log

KIDS: Whenever there is a guest speaker or missionary, ask him to sign his name and favorite Scripture reference.

Guest Speaker	Scripture Reference

Guest Speaker Log

KIDS: Whenever there is a guest speaker or missionary, ask him to sign his name and favorite Scripture reference.

Guest Speaker	Scripture Reference
Guest Speaker	Scripture Reference
Guest Speaker	Scripture Reference
Guest Speaker	Scripture Reference
Guest Speaker	Scripture Reference
Guest Speaker	Scripture Reference
Guest Speaker	Scripture Reference
Guest Speaker	Scripture Reference
Guest Speaker	Scripture Reference
Guest Speaker	Scripture Reference
Guest Speaker	Scripture Reference
Guest Speaker	Scripture Reference
Guest Speaker	Scripture Reference
Guest Speaker	Scripture Reference
Guest Speaker	Scripture Reference
Guest Speaker	Scripture Reference
Guest Speaker	Scripture Reference